Introduction　　　　　　小学校 Version

　本書は、長年、中学校で英語授業を行ってきた坂本先生と ALT ミシェルによるティーム・ティーチング授業の帯活動をまとめた一冊です。チャンツ、ALT との発音トレーニング、Teacher Talk のリスニング、"友達 Match (Speed Friends)"で文法復習のシンプル英会話、発展的コミュニケーション活動、活発 Negotiation など、付属の QR コードから動画や音声、画像を取得しながら学習できるスタイルです。動画では、ミシェルが Vtuber avatar "Teacher Amy"、坂本先生が"Nami-sensei"となって学習をサポートします。帯活動とは、授業に毎回取り入れる一連の意味を持った活動を指します。帯活動を重ねることで、英語授業にリズムが生まれ、学習者にとって安定した環境と確実な学習の定着を図ることができます。

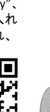

　また、下のカテゴリー表を用いて、各帯活動が、「読む・聞く・話す［やり取り］・話す［発表］・書く」のどの技能に焦点を当てているか、「知識・技能」「思考・判断・表現」「主体的に学習に取り組む態度」のいずれの力の育成を目指しているかを確認することができ、英語教師にも学習者にも活動の目的が直感でわかるようになっています。4 技能 5 領域＋コミュニケーション力をバランスよく向上するのに役立つ一冊。Now, let's start English class!

＜各帯活動が関わる領域と評価の観点＞

帯活動	読む	聞く	発表	やり取り	書く	知識・技能	思考・判断・表現	主体的に取り組む態度
1　ヒント Quiz	○	○	○	○	○	○	○	○
2　発音 Revolution	○	○				○		
3　友達 Match (Speed Friends)	○	○	○	○	○	○	○	○
4　探究 Quiz	○	○	(○)			○	○	○
5　上達 Chants	○	○	(○)			○		○
6　熟練 Sound Connection	○	○	(○)	○		○	○	○
7　伝言 Message	○	○		(○)	○	○		○
8　あいづち Comment Reading	○	○	(○)	○		○	○	○

ヒント Quiz

Hint Quiz

ここでは、ペアの相手にある「もの・人・動物など」についての説明を英語で行い、クイズをだしていきましょう。

1. ヒント Quiz の答えを考え、短い説明文を３文以上で考える。
2. ペアになってヒントを出し合い、相手の答えを当て合う。

In this activity, students explain an object, person, animal, etc. to their partner in English.

1. Think of an answer and at least 3 sentences to explain it.
2. Make pairs. Listen to your partner's hints & try to guess the answer.

4 技能 5 領域					評価の観点		
読む	聞く	発表	やり取り	書く	知識・技能	思考・判断・表現	主体的に取り組む態度
○	○	○	○	○	○	○	○

< One more try! >

目に見えるもの（pen, apple, dog, restaurant など）から目に見えないもの（dream, AI, job など）まで、幅広くチャレンジしていきましょう。友達どうして発表し合うとより多くのヒントを聞くことになり、次のヒント Quiz づくりを考える「ヒント」がもらえますね。

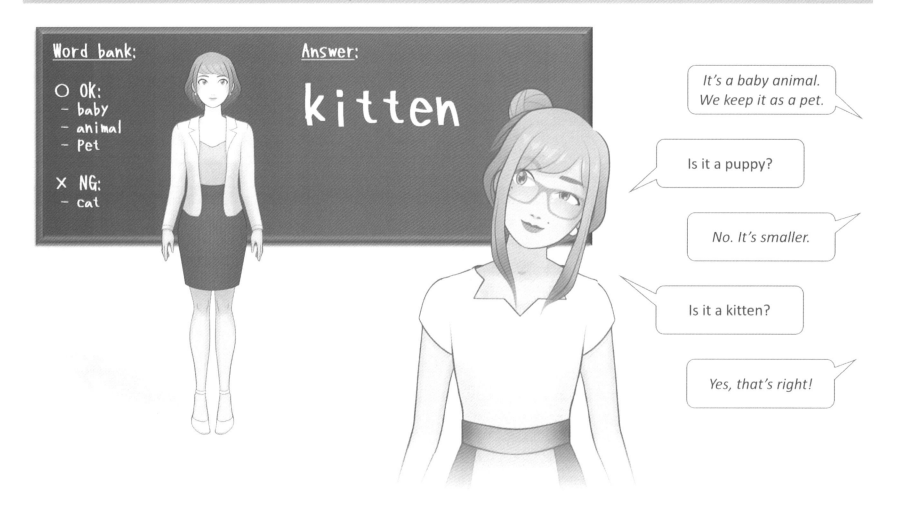

発音 Revolution

Hatsuon Revolution

ここでは、英語の発音を聞き分ける練習をしましょう。

Practice differentiating between similar English sounds.

1. QR コードからアクセスし、音を聞き分ける練習として、その音の違いを意識しながら繰り返す。
2. クイズの音声を聞いて、表の中の聞き取った単語のほうを〇で囲む。
3. 答え合わせをし、結果を表の下段の得点表に書き込む。
4. 音声に基づいたクイズの出題方法をまねしながら、ペアでクイズを出し合う。

1. Access videos by QR code. Listen to the recordings, paying attention to the difference between sounds.
2. Listen to the recorded quiz & circle the words you hear (choose from the table).
3. Check your answers. Calculate your points & write them at the bottom of the table.
4. Try practicing with a partner by imitating the style of the recorded quizzes.

4技能5領域					評価の観点		
読む	聞く	発表	やり取り	書く	知識・技能	思考・判断・表現	主体的に取り組む態度
〇	〇				〇		〇

< One More Try! >

発音の違いに気づいたら、できるだけたくさん自分で発音してみましょう。ペアで出題し合う時は、まず自分の答えを設定し、じゃんけんで出題者と解答者の順番を決めて、互いに出題し合いましょう。口元を隠して発音するのがコツです。

発音 Revolution　☠ Pirate or pilot? ✈

Which do you hear, **/r/** or **/l/**?　Circle your answer.

	ROUND 1		2		3		4		5	
Normal (1 点)			r	l	r	l	r	l	r	l
1	right (右)	light (光)	right	light	right	light	right	light	right	light
2	red (赤い)	led (導いた)	red	led	red	led	red	led	red	led
3	wrong (間違った)	long (長い)	wrong	long	wrong	long	wrong	long	wrong	long
4	rice (米)	lice (しらみ)	rice	lice	rice	lice	rice	lice	rice	lice
5	races (競走)	laces (ひも)	races	laces	races	laces	races	laces	races	laces
Challenge (2 点)				l	r	l	r	l	r	l
6	pirate (海賊)	pilot (パイロット)	pirate	pilot	pirate	pilot	pirate	pilot	pirate	pilot
7	arrive (着く)	alive (生きている)	arrive	alive	arrive	alive	arrive	alive	arrive	alive
8	brush (筆)	blush (紅潮)	brush	blush	brush	blush	brush	blush	brush	blush
9	fruit (果物)	flute (フルート)	fruit	flute	fruit	flute	fruit	flute	fruit	flute
10	pray (祈る)	play (遊ぶ)	pray	play	pray	play	pray	play	pray	play
			/15 点		/15 点		/15 点		/15 点		/15 点

発音 Revolution ☒ <u>V</u>ote or <u>b</u>oat?

Which do you hear, **/v/** or **/b/**? (Circle) your answer.

	ROUND 1		2		3		4		5	
Normal (1 点)			v	b	v	b	v	b	v	b
1	vote (投票)	boat (船)	vote	boat	vote	boat	vote	boat	vote	boat
2	vet (獣医師)	bet (賭ける)	vet	bet	vet	bet	vet	bet	vet	bet
3	very (とても)	berry (木の実)	very	berry	very	berry	very	berry	very	berry
4	vow (信約)	bow (お辞儀)	vow	bow	vow	bow	vow	bow	vow	bow
5	vigor (精力、活発)	bigger (〜より大きい)	vigor	bigger	vigor	bigger	vigor	bigger	vigor	bigger
Challenge (2 点)			v	b	v	b	v	b	v	b
6	revel (大きいに楽しむ)	rebel (反逆者)	revel	rebel	revel	rebel	revel	rebel	revel	rebel
7	covered (ふたのある)	cupboard (食器棚)	covered	cupboard	covered	cupboard	covered	cupboard	covered	cupboard
8	curve (曲線)	curb (歩道の縁石)	curve	curb	curve	curb	curve	curb	curve	curb
9	dove (ハト)	dub (吹き替え)	dove	dub	dove	dub	dove	dub	dove	dub
10	jive (スイング音楽)	jibe (ジャイブする)	jive	jibe	jive	jibe	jive	jibe	jive	jibe
		/15 点		/15 点		/15 点		/15 点		/15 点

発音 Revolution ✝ Faith or face? ☺

Which do you hear, **/θ/** or **/s/**? Circle your answer.

	ROUND 1		2		3		4		5	
Normal (1 点)			θ	s	θ	s	θ	s	θ	s
1	thank (感謝する)	sank (sink の過去形)	thank	sank	thank	sank	thank	sank	thank	sank
2	think (考える)	sink (沈む)	think	sink	think	sink	think	sink	think	sink
3	thin (細い)	sin (罪)	thin	sin	thin	sin	thin	sin	thin	sin
4	thick (厚い)	sick (病気の)	thick	sick	thick	sick	thick	sick	thick	sick
5	theme (テーマ)	seem (〜に見える)	theme	seem	theme	seem	theme	seem	theme	seem
Challenge (2 点)				s	θ	s	θ	s	θ	s
6	bath (お風呂)	bass (バス [魚])	bath	bass	bath	bass	bath	bass	bath	bass
7	youth (若さ)	use (使用すること)	youth	use	youth	use	youth	use	youth	use
8	path (道)	pass (パス)	path	pass	path	pass	path	pass	path	pass
9	faith (信念)	face (顔)	faith	face	faith	face	faith	face	faith	face
10	myth (神話)	miss (的を外す)	myth	miss	myth	miss	myth	miss	myth	miss
	/15 点		/15 点		/15 点		/15 点		/15 点	

発音 Revolution　　📄 Sheet or seat? ✏️

Which do you hear, **/ʃ/** or **/s/**? (Circle) your answer.

	ROUND 1		2		3		4		5	
Normal (1 点)		ʃ	s	ʃ	s	ʃ	s	ʃ	s	
1	sheet (枚)　　seat (座席)	sheet	seat	sheet	seat	sheet	seat	sheet	seat
2	she (彼女は　　sea (海)	she	sea	she	sea	she	sea	she	sea
3	sheep (羊)　　seep (しみ出る)	sheep	seep	sheep	seep	sheep	seep	sheep	seep
4	ship (船)　　sip (少しずつ飲む)	ship	sip	ship	sip	ship	sip	ship	sip
5	shin (すね)　　sin (罪)	shin	sin	shin	sin	shin	sin	shin	sin
Challenge (2 点)		ʃ	s	ʃ	s	ʃ	s	ʃ	s	
6	mash (すりつぶす)　　mass (塊)	mash	mass	mash	mass	mash	mass	mash	mass
7	mesh (網の目)　　mess (寄せ集め)	mesh	mess	mesh	mess	mesh	mess	mesh	mess
8	fashion (流行)　　fasten (留める)	fashion	fasten	fashion	fasten	fashion	fasten	fashion	fasten
9	fished (釣られた)　　fist (拳)	fished	fist	fished	fist	fished	fist	fished	fist
10	crushed (押しつぶされた)　　crust (パンの表面)	crushed	crust	crushed	crust	crushed	crust	crushed	crust
	/15 点		/15 点		/15 点		/15 点		/15 点	

発音 Revolution

 Green or grin?

Which do you hear, **/iː/** or **/i/**? Circle your answer.

	ROUND 1		2		3		4		5	
Normal (1 点)			iː	i	iː	i	iː	i	iː	i
1	green (代の緑)	grin (にこやかな笑顔)	green	grin	green	grin	green	grin	green	grin
2	teen (10 代の)	tin (錫)	teen	tin	teen	tin	teen	tin	teen	tin
3	sheep (ヒツジ)	ship (船)	sheep	ship	sheep	ship	sheep	ship	sheep	ship
4	wheel (車輪)	will (〜するつもりである)	wheel	will	wheel	will	wheel	will	wheel	will
5	seat (座席)	sit (座る)	seat	sit	seat	sit	seat	sit	seat	sit
Challenge (2 点)			i	iː	i	iː	i	iː	i	iː
6	heats (温める)	hits (打つ丘[複])	heats	hits	heats	hits	heats	hits	heats	hits
7	heels (かかと[複])	hills (丘[複])	heels	hills	heels	hills	heels	hills	heels	hills
8	deeper (より深い)	dipper (ひしゃく)	deeper	dipper	deeper	dipper	deeper	dipper	deeper	dipper
9	peeler (皮むき器)	pillar (支柱)	peeler	pillar	peeler	pillar	peeler	pillar	peeler	pillar
10	leaving (leave の現在分詞)	living (live の現在分詞)	leaving	living	leaving	living	leaving	living	leaving	living
			/15 点		/15 点		/15 点		/15 点		/15 点

発音 Revolution } Cut or cat? {

Which do you hear, /ʌ/ or /æ/? (Circle) your answer.

#	ROUND 1		2		3		4		5	
	ʌ	æ	ʌ	æ	ʌ	æ	ʌ	æ	ʌ	æ
Normal (1点)										
1	cut (切る)	cat (猫)	cut	cat	cut	cat	cut	cat	cut	cat
2	fun (楽しい)	fan (扇子)	fun	fan	fun	fan	fun	fan	fun	fan
3	much (たくさん)	match (試合)	much	match	much	match	much	match	much	match
4	bug (虫)	bag (鞄、袋)	bug	bag	bug	bag	bug	bag	bug	bag
5	bun (丸いパン)	ban (禁じる)	bun	ban	bun	ban	bun	ban	bun	ban
Challenge (2点)										
6	butter (バター)	batter (打者)	butter	batter	butter	batter	butter	batter	butter	batter
7	stunned (ぼう然として)	stand (立つ)	stunned	stand	stunned	stand	stunned	stand	stunned	stand
8	puddle (水たまり)	paddle (櫂)	puddle	paddle	puddle	paddle	puddle	paddle	puddle	paddle
9	begun (begin の過去分詞)	began (begin の過去分詞)	begun	began	begun	began	begun	began	begun	began
10	uncle (叔父)	ankle (足首)	uncle	ankle	uncle	ankle	uncle	ankle	uncle	ankle
	/15点		/15点		/15点		/15点		/15点	

友達 Match　　　　　　　　　　　(Speed Friends)

ここでは、できるだけたくさんの人と会話をして、一番共通点の多い人を探しましょう。

1. 今日の英文１文を声に出して読み、内容を確認する。
2. 「Me」の欄に自分の答えを書き込む。
3. 先生の合図で、一人目の人とペアを組み、じゃんけんをする。勝った人が聞き、負けた人が応える。
4. 聞き手は自分の応えも相手に伝えて、自分の答えと同じだったら〇、違っていたらＸを表に書き込む。
5. 先生の合図があったら、「Thank you!」と今のペアの相手に伝えて、次のペアへ移る。
6. ５人の相手と会話をしたら、一番〇の多かった人について、表の下段に英語で紹介する。

Speak to as many people as possible, searching for people you have the most in common with.

1. Read today's sentence out loud, checking the contents.
2. Write your own answers under "Me."
3. At the teacher's signal, find a partner & play rock, paper, scissors. The winner asks, the loser answers.
4. Both partners should share their answers. If your answer is the same, mark it with a "〇". If different, an "X".
5. At the teacher's signal, tell your partner "Thank you!" and make your next pair.
6. After speaking with 5 people, write about your "Top Match" at the bottom of the table.

4 技能 5 領域					評価の規準		
読む	聞く	発表	やり取り	書く	知識・技能	思考・判断・表現	主体的に取り組む態度
〇	〇	〇	〇	〇	〇	〇	〇

< One More Try! >

相手の質問に１文だけで答えるだけでなく、２文以上にチャレンジしましょう。質問者は、相手の返事にリアクションをしましょう。

友達 Match (Speed Friends)

No. 1	me	ex.	1	2	3	4	5
		Aika					
① Do you like sweets?		yes (ice cream)					
② Do you play the piano?		yes (8 y/o)					
③ Can you skate fast?		no					
④ When is your birthday?		May 19					
⑤ What do you want for your birthday?		a game					
Top Match							

I found ( ).

He/She and I ( ).

友達 Match　　　　　　　　　　　(Speed Friends)

		me	Ayana	1	2	3	4	5
①	Do you like Japanese pop music?		yes (Arashi)					
②	What color do you like?		green					
③	Do you have music class on Wednesday?		no (Thurs)					
④	Can you say "隣の客はよく柿食う客だ" three times fast?		no					
⑤	When do you study English?		after dinner					

Top Match

I found (　　　　　　　　　　　　　　　　　　　　　　).

He/She and I (　　　　　　　　　　　　　　　　　　　).

友達 Match (Speed Friends)

No. 3

	me	ex.	1	2	3	4	5
		Katsunori					
① Do you like summer?		no (too hot)					
② What do you want to eat in summer?		ice cream					
③ Do you like winter?		yes					
④ What do you want to do in winter?		go skiing					
⑤ Where do you want to go in spring?		Himeji					

Top Match

I found ( ).

He/She and I ( ).

友達 Match　　　　　　　　　　(Speed Friends)

		me	ex. Kokoro	1	2	3	4	5
①	Are you good at cooking?		no					
②	Can you make sushi well?		no					
③	What do you eat on New Year's Day?		cake					
④	What is your favorite Japanese food?		onigiri					
⑤	What is your favorite Italian food?		pizza					

Top Match

I found (　　　　　　　　　　　　　　　　　　　　　　　).

He/She and I (　　　　　　　　　　　　　　　　　　　　).

友達 Match (Speed Friends)

No. 5

	me	ex. Ryusei	1	2	3	4	5
① Where do you study at home?		in my room					
② Do you often play video games?		once a week					
③ What is your favorite animation?		One Piece					
④ What do you usually do on Sundays?		watch TV					
⑤ When is your favorite day of the week?		Friday					

Top Match

I found ( ).

He/She and I ( ).

6

友達 Match   (Speed Friends)

No. 6		me	Taiyo	1	2	3	4	5
①	Where do you want to go in the world?		Korea					
②	Do you want to go there by airplane, or by ship?		plane					
③	What do you want to see there?		culture & fashion					
④	Where do you want to go in Japan?		Kyoto					
⑤	Why do you want to go there?		to see temples					

Top Match

I found (   ).

He/She and I (   ).

友達 Match   (Speed Friends)

No. 7		me	ex.	1	2	3	4	5
			Takeshi					
①	What did you do last Sunday?		watched TV					
②	Did you enjoy your weekend?		yes					
③	Do you like camping in the mountains?		yes					
④	What animal do you like?		tigers					
⑤	Do you have any pets?		yes (fish)					

Top Match

I found (   ).

He/She and I (   ).

友達 Match   (Speed Friends)

		me	Yoshito	1	2	3	4	5
①	Are you hungry now?		yes					
②	What did you eat last night?		ramen					
③	Do you often eat curry and rice?		yes					
④	What food do you like the best?		pizza					
⑤	What do you want to eat for dinner tonight?		hot pot					

Top Match

I found (   ).

He/She and I (   ).

探究 Quiz

ここでは、ペアで相手に質問をしていき、相手が選択している単語を当てましょう。

1. 「Word Bank」内の単語を使って、個人で「あるもの・人・動物など」についてのヒントを作成する
2. ペアになってじゃんけんをして、勝った人からどんどん質問をして、答えを探る
3. 負けた人の返事を聞きながら、勝っている相手が正解を当てていく

徐々に「Word Bank」内の言葉は少なくなっていくので、徐々に自分たちでオリジナルの質問や回答を探して答えを探していく。

Tankyu Quiz

In this activity, ask your partner questions and try to guess the vocabulary word they have chosen.

1. Using the "Word Bank," make your own hints about your chosen topic (thing, person, animal, etc.)
2. Play rock-paper-scissors in pairs. Starting with the winner, ask questions to get hints.
3. While listening to the replies of the other partner, they will try to guess the answer.

As the number of words in "Word Bank" gradually decreases, we will begin to search for answers using original questions and answers.

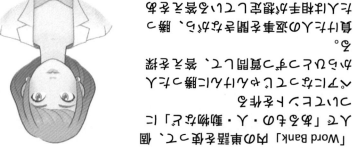

4技能5領域					評価の観点		
読む	聞く	発表	やり取り	書く	知識・技能	思考・判断・表現	主体的に取り組む態度
○	○	(○)	○	○	○	○	○

< One More Try! >

質問をする際には、yes/No で答える質問から、5W1H(Who/what/When/Where/Why/How)を使って答える範囲を幅広く使っていきましょう。

What is this animal?

What continent does it live in? → *It lives in South America.*
What does it look like? → *It has long claws & brown fur.*
What does it like to do? → *It often sleeps in trees.* ※

Choose 2 more animals & use the word bank to write about them!
Your friend will ask you questions & try to guess.

It lives in… North America / South America / Africa / Europe / Asia / Australia and Oceania / Antarctica / Japan / the forest / the mountains / the city
It has… legs / paws / claws / fur / scales / feathers / a tail / wings / fins / spots / stripes
It likes to… play / sleep / eat / hunt / run
It's a(n)… wolf / bear / elephant / camel / snake / owl / leopard / tiger / lion / shark / dolphin / whale / cow / raccoon / fox / koala / turtle

①

②

※ *Answer: It's a sloth!*

探究 Quiz

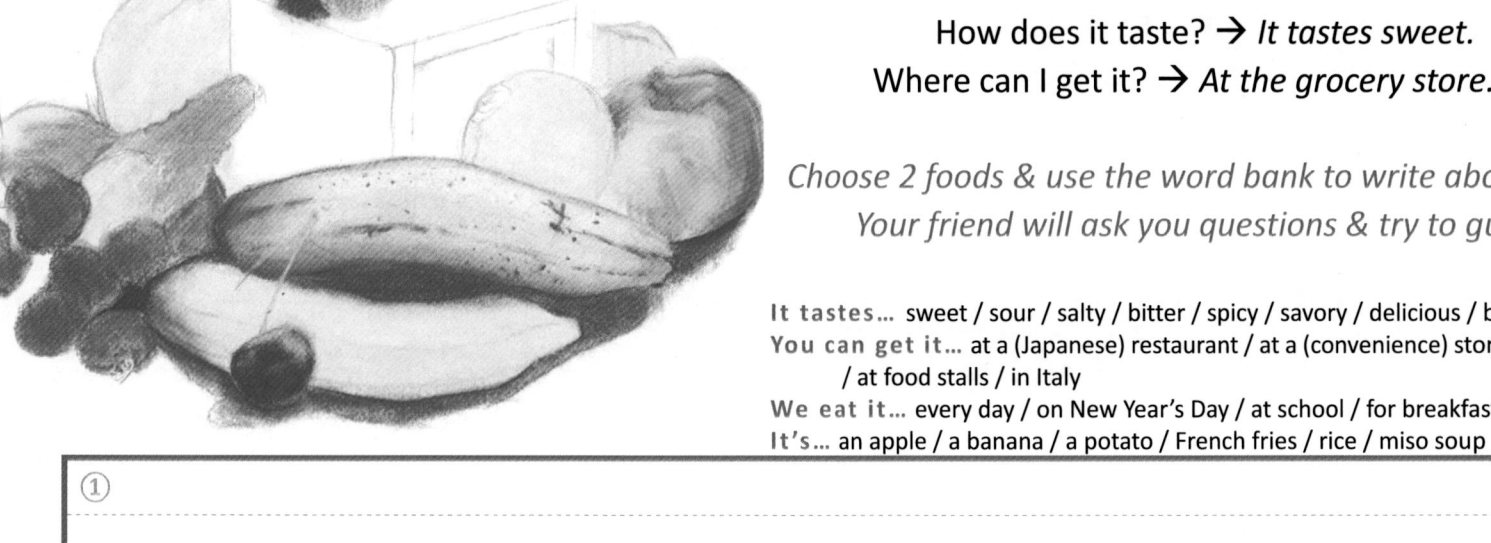

What is this food?

What color is it? → *It's red.*
How does it taste? → *It tastes sweet.*
Where can I get it? → *At the grocery store.* ※

Choose 2 foods & use the word bank to write about them!
Your friend will ask you questions & try to guess.

It tastes… sweet / sour / salty / bitter / spicy / savory / delicious / bad
You can get it… at a (Japanese) restaurant / at a (convenience) store / at a bakery
　　　　　　/ at food stalls / in Italy
We eat it… every day / on New Year's Day / at school / for breakfast / as a snack
It's… an apple / a banana / a potato / French fries / rice / miso soup

①

②

※ *Answer: It's an apple!*

上達 Chants   Jotatsu Chants

一定のリズムにフレーズを乗せて発話し、繰り返してフレーズを何度も聞く活動です。イントネーションや強弱に慣れていきましょう。

In this activity, students repeat phrases several times, following a set rhythm. This helps them get used to intonation & word stress.

1. QR コードからアクセスし、音声を聞く。
2. 音声をまねて発話し、リズムとイントネーションをつかむ。
3. 音声と一緒に発話する。(慣れてくると、ペアやグループで担当箇所をもうけて発話したり、一文ずつ順に回したりしてもよい。)

1. Access videos by QR code & listen to the recording.
2. Mimic the recording, enunciating the rhythm & intonation.
3. Speak with the recording. (After becoming used to it, try doing the chant with a pair or group. It can work well to assign parts or alternate word by word.)

4 技能 5 領域					評価の規準		
読む	聞く	発表	やり取り	書く	知識・技能	思考・判断・表現	主体的に取り組む態度
○	○	(○)			○		○

< One More Try! >

リズムよく言えるようになったら、互いに発表したり、そのフレーズを使った会話をしたりしてみましょう。

上達 Chants

Birthday Months

A:　　When is your birthday?

B:　　It's April 1st.

A:　　That's nice! It's the month of blooming trees.

B:　　And how about yours?

A:　　It's October 3rd.

B:　　That's great! It's the month of falling leaves.

Birthday Present

A:　　What do you want for your birthday present?

B:　　I want a new book for my birthday present.

A:　　When do you read in your daily life?

B:　　I read before bed, so I sleep well all night.

School Tour Chant

A: I want to know about this school. I want to walk around the school.

B: Tell me where you want to go. I'll take you on a campus tour!

A: Please tell me, where's the library?   B: It's next to the door, on the very first floor.

A: Please tell me, where is our homeroom class?   B: It's one of five rooms on the second floor.

A: Please tell me, where is the music room?   B: It's my favorite place, on the third floor.

上達 Chants

Weekend Chant

              *   *   *   *
A: What do you usually do on the weekend?

           *   *   *   *
B: I like to go shopping with all of my friends.

           *   *   *   *
A: Where do you usually go with your friends?

                 *   *   *   *
B: To bookstores, a food court and stationary shops.

           *   *   *   *
A: What is your favorite stationary shop?

                 *   *   *   *
B: In my town, I have two favorite stationary shops.

           *   *   *   *
A: Next time you go, can I come shopping, too?

                 *   *   *   *
B: Of course! I want to shop with you!

Aquarium Chant

        *   *   *   *

A: How was your vacation? Where did you go? What did you do?

         *   *   *   *

B: I went to the aquarium. It's nice, big, and near my house.

          *   *   *   *

A: You went to the aquarium? What kinds of animals did you see?

         *   *

B: Jumping dolphins, swimming sharks,

        *   *

          walking penguins and tropical fish.

           *   *

A: That sounds like an amazing time!

          *   *

B: Now, tell me. How was your vacation?

熟練 Sound Connection　　Jukuren Sound Connection

ここでは、リンキングを練習し、各文を発端として会話につなげていきましょう。

1. QR コードからアクセスし、音声を聞く。太字のリンキング部分を繰り返し練習する。
2. 自然なイントネーションで発話できているかを確認する。
3. できるだけたくさんの人と会話をする。ペアの相手とじゃんけんをし、勝った人が提示文を使って会話を始める。ペアの間で 2 往復以上の会話ができたら、「Thank you!」と声をかけ、お互いのサイン枠にサインをして別れ、次のペアへ移る。
4. 終了の合図があったら席に着き、サインの数をカウントして記入する。

Here, students will practice linking sounds in a conversation.

1. Access the recordings by QR code. Practice the bold, connected sounds several times.
2. Make sure you speak with natural intonation.
3. Talk to as many people as possible. Make pairs and play rock-paper-scissors. The winner starts. Have a conversation with at least 2 exchanges, then say, "Thank you!" Exchange signatures, then change pairs.
4. When the teacher signals the end of the activity, count the number of signatures you collected.

4技能5領域					評価の観点		
読む	聞く	発表	やり取り	書く	知識・技能	思考・判断・表現	主体的に取り組む態度
○	○	(○)	○		○	○	○

< One More Try! >

英語の音については、いろいろな変化があります。・linking（連結）…単語と単語がつながり、音が連結すること・intrusion（介入）…次の音に介入すること・elision（脱落）…単語の中の発音されるはずの音が発音されないこと・assimilation（同化）…後ろの子音の音とくっついて１つの音になったり、子音が変化したりすること・geminates（重複）…音が重複した時に最初の音が軽く発音されること

Connection Type 1: Linking

1) What are you doing this evening? → *whatare / thisevening*	2) Do you have any pets? → *haveany*	3) Which are better: cats or dogs? → *whichare / catsor*
SIGNATURES:	SIGNATURES:	SIGNATURES:
TOTAL NUMBER:	TOTAL NUMBER:	TOTAL NUMBER:

Connection Type 2: Intrusion

1) Can I ask you a question?	2) Where do you go out to eat?	3) Do you enjoy sports?
→ *I ask / youwa*	→ *gowout / toweat*	→ *youwenjoy*
SIGNATURES:	SIGNATURES:	SIGNATURES:
TOTAL NUMBER:	TOTAL NUMBER:	TOTAL NUMBER:

伝言 Message   Dengon Message

Amy 先生のストーリーテリングを聞きながら、内容理解を深めていきましょう。

1. QR コードからアクセスし、 Amy 先生のストーリーテリングを聞く。
2. 1 度目は、何も書かずに流して概要を掴む。
3. 2 度目は、ワークブックの英文内の（　　　）にあてはまる語を書き取る。
4. 3 度目は、（　　　）内の語を確認しながら、再度聞く。

Listen to Amy's storytelling, focusing on understanding the contents.

1. Access the video recordings through the QR code.
2. 1st Listen: Listen without writing anything to get the overall meaning.
3. 2nd Listen: Write your answers in the blanks in the workbook.
4. 3rd Listen: Check your answers.

4技能5領域					評価の観点		
読む	聞く	発表	やり取り	書く	知識・技能	思考・判断・表現	主体的に取り組む態度
○	○		(○)	○	○		○

< One More Try! >

（　　　）内の語句を確認し、内容が把握できたら、シャドーイングにチャレンジしてみましょう。英語らしい音のつながりやイントネーションを身に付けることができます。

Summer Vacation

選択肢：them / some / We / summer / very / What / Do / His / He / We

This (1) _____ vacation, I went to Hokkaido and Tohoku.

(2) _____ did I do? First, I went to Hokkaido with my friend.

(3) _____ name is James. (4) _____ is from England. It was his

first time in Japan. (5) _____ liked the hot springs very much.

Second, in Aomori Prefecture, I saw the Nebuta Festival.

(6) _____ you know it? The floats were (7) _____ beautiful. I

said, "Rassera, rassera!" Third, in Akita Prefecture, I saw the

Kanto Festival. I have (8) _____ friends in Akita Prefecture. I

visited (9) _____. (10) _____ had a lot of fun at the festival.

伝言 Message

Cat Cafés

選択肢：wash / name / live / nice / very / have / went / live / surprise / play

Do you know about "cat cafés"? They are like normal cafés, but cats _____(1) there. Customers can _____(2) with them. I heard about cat cafés recently. I was _____(3) surprised. In Canada, we don't _____(4) them. I was in Tokyo in August.

I _____(5) to a cat café in Akihabara. The _____(6) is NekoJaLaLa. Eight cute cats _____(7) there. It's important to be _____(8) to the cats. The café has a guidebook. You have to follow the rules. Rule 1: _____(9) your hands before touching the cats. Rule 2: do not _____(10) the cats. Cat cafés are a lot of fun.

Scripts

1. Summer Vacation

This summer(1) vacation, I went to Hokkaido and Tohoku. What(2) did I do? First, I went to Hokkaido with my friend. His(3) name is James. He(4) is from England. It was his first time in Japan. We(5) liked the hot springs very much. Second, in Aomori Prefecture, I saw the Nebuta Festival. Do(6) you know it? The floats were very(7) beautiful. I said, "Rassera, rassera!" Third, in Akita Prefecture, I saw the Kanto Festival. I have some(8) friends in Akita Prefecture. I visited them(9). We(10) had a lot of fun at the festival.

2. Cat Cafés

Do you know about "cat cafés"? They are like normal cafés, but cats live (1) there. Customers can play (2) with them. I heard about cat cafés recently. I was very (3) surprised. In Canada, we don't have (4) them. I went (5) to a cat café in Akihabara. The name (6) is Nekojalala. Eight cute cats live (7) there. It's important to be nice (8) to the cats. The café has a guidebook. You have to follow the rules. Rule 1: wash (9) your hands before touching the cats. Rule 2: do not surprise (10) the cats. Cat cafés are a lot of fun.

あいづち Comment Reading　　Aizuchi Comment Reading

前のセクション「伝言 Message」の本文を使って、ペアの相手の話に相づちをうったり、話を広げたりしましょう。

1. ペアでそれぞれ「伝言 Message」を読む練習をする。
2. じゃんけんをして、話し手と相づちをうつ人を決める。
3. 話し手がメッセージを読み始めるが、1 文読むたびにペアの相手はあいづちを入れていく。
4. 一通り読めたら交代をする。

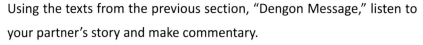

Using the texts from the previous section, "Dengon Message," listen to your partner's story and make commentary.

1. Practice reading "Dengon Message" as a pair.
2. Play rock-paper-scissors to decide roles.
3. Read the text one sentence at a time. After each sentence, insert one comment.
4. When finished, switch roles.

<使える英語表現集> I see. / Oh, really? / I didn't know that. / That's interesting! / I can't believe it. / Tell me more. / Wow! / Is it true? / I think that ( ). / It's ( ). / I don't think so. / How ( ) it is! / What a ( ) it is! / What do you ( )? / Why ( )? / How many ( )? など

4技能5領域					評価の観点		
読む	聞く	発表	やり取り	書く	知識・技能	思考・判断・表現	主体的に取り組む態度
○	○	(○)	○		○	○	○

< One More Try! >

短い相づちに加えて、質問をしたりコメントを返したりしながら、自然な会話になるように話題を広げていくこともできます。また、友達同士で発表するのもいいでしょう。

This summer vacation, I went to Hokkaido and Tohoku.

That's nice!

What did I do?

Tell me more.

First, I went to Hokkaido with my friend.

What did you do there?